Lost in the Snow

by Claire Alexander

For
Beautiful Mia

First published in Great Britain in 2010 by
Gullane Children's Books
185 Fleet Street, London, EC4A 2HS
www.gullanebooks.com

1   3   5   7   9   10   8   6   4   2

Text and illustrations © Claire Alexander 2010

The right of Claire Alexander to be identified as the author and illustrator of
this work has been asserted by her in accordance with the Copyright, Designs and Patents Act, 1988.

A CIP record for this title is available from the British Library.

ISBN: 978-1-86233-731-2

Printed and bound in China

Lost in the Snow

by Claire Alexander

GULLANE
CHILDREN'S BOOKS

One day in winter,
two fox cubs watched the
snowfall for the first time.

Mother Fox said,
"You can go out and play,
as long as you stay
where I can see you."

Benny was the first to leave the den.
He was so excited, he jumped head-first into the snow.

Fern followed a little more carefully. First she peeped out . . .

then she sniffed the snow . . .

and then she tested it with her paw.
Finally she was ready to venture out.

Fern made lots of lovely neat tracks in the snow,
while Benny kicked it up all over the place.
"This is so much fun!" he cried.

Just then, they heard a noise in the distance –
a swoosh and wheee!
coming from over the hill.

"What's that?" asked Fern.
"Let's go and see!" said Benny.

"Mummy said to stay close,"
said Fern.

But Benny was already
too far away to hear her.

"Come back, Benny!" Fern cried.

But Benny kept going, further and further . . .

and further until . . .

"Look!" cried Benny . . .

wheeee

swoosh

swoosh

"Ice-skating hares!"

It looked so much fun, Fern forgot to tell
Benny that Mummy might be worried.

And when Benny raced down the hill . . .

Fern followed.

"Hello! Come and join us," called the hares.
"We'll teach you to skate!"

Soon Fern and Benny were
whizzing about on the ice.
"Wheeeeee!" cried Benny.
"This is so much fun!" laughed Fern.

Eventually the sun started to go down.
It was time for the hares to go home.
"We should go home too, Benny," said Fern, as she
remembered what their mummy had said to them.

So they raced back up the hill.
"Which way now?" asked Fern.

Benny didn't know.
"WE ARE LOST!" he cried.

Benny was scared.

Fern was scared too.

But then something caught her eye. . .

"I remember that pretty flower!" said Fern. "This is the way home!"

"Come on, Benny – follow me!" she called. "Mind your head . . .

and watch out for the tree stump!"

And before they knew it, there was . . .

Mummy!

"You naughty little cubs, where have you been?"
she scolded. "I was so worried about you!"

"We're sorry, Mummy,"
said Fern and Benny.
"We'll never run away again."

"I'm just so pleased to have you back,"
said Mummy, as she hugged her
little cubs tightly to her.

After that Benny was a little more sensible,
and Fern was a little less timid. And both of them
had lots more fun in the snow!